THE OLDEST MAN
IN AMERICA

THE OLDEST MAN
IN AMERICA

An Adventure in Archaeology

RUTH KIRK

Foreword by
Professors Roald Fryxell and Richard Daugherty

With photographs by
Ruth and Louis Kirk

HARCOURT BRACE JOVANOVICH, INC.
New York

ILLUSTRATION CREDITS: Drawing on page 11, Roald Fryxell; page 21, Washington State University photo by Jim Barker, courtesy of Dr. Roderick Sprague; p. 23, Washington State University photo by Robert Bullis; page 61, U.S. Geological Survey photo by Frank Forester; pages 90 and 92, Washington State University photos by Roald Fryxell; page 91, Washington State University photo by Harvey S. Rice.

Copyright © 1970 by Ruth Kirk

FIRST EDITION
Hardbound edition ISBN 0-15-257830-7
Library edition ISBN 0-15-257831-5
Library of Congress Catalog Card Number: 73-117617

PRINTED IN THE UNITED STATES OF AMERICA

To the *Hon. Warren G. Magnuson*
UNITED STATES SENATE

who not only appreciates our prehistoric heritage
but has cared enough to do something about it

CONTENTS

Professors Richard Daugherty and Roald Fryxell

FOREWORD

In the wake of the massive and desperate struggle to save the Marmes Archaeological Site, there is now time to consider the full significance of events during the frantic months between May, 1968, when the emergency salvage operation began, and February, 1969, when it ended—bleakly—as the rising waters of Lower Monumental Reservoir drowned the site. It is increasingly clear as time passes that the remnants dug from within the earth in this southeast corner of Washington have importance far beyond the items themselves.

The scientific importance of the Marmes Rock Shelter far exceeds the fact that it yielded remains as old as those discovered there in 1968. Its true significance lies in the *sequence* of prehistory recorded: a detailed record of 18,000 or 20,000 years of geologic events with an interwoven record of human occupation spanning more than half those millennia, documented by the fragile remains of nearly thirty individuals who lived and died at the rock shelter, as well as by the tools they fashioned and by the bones of the animals they killed and cooked and ate. The record is dramatic, and its contribution to understanding our own unique time in history is great. Yet the significance of events at Marmes concerns the future as well as the past.

For the first time in this country, national scientific, public, and political concern reached from a remote western canyon to the President of the United States, urging protection for an archaeological example of our cultural heritage. When ground was broken to begin construction of a levee, built in response to the demand, guests present for the occasion included local ranchers, a United

States Senator, educators and businessmen, children, and delegates from almost every major scientific organization in North America representing archaeology and geology.

Thus the Marmes site has made a contribution to the American public beyond its own remarkable record of our prehistory. It has stimulated a deep awareness of the value and urgency of caring for the rapidly vanishing traces of our natural and cultural resources throughout the continent. As dams and roads are built, as cities expand, as thoughtless collectors plunder the limited number of sites, steps must be taken—immediately—to safeguard this dwindling legacy before it is irretrievably gone. The information remaining in sites not yet destroyed must be systematically recovered, protected, and interpreted for the benefit of everyone. When this work is properly financed and an adequate national program is authorized and under way, the appraisal of Senator Warren G. Magnuson in connection with Marmes will come true. He called the action to preserve this one site, "a landmark precedent in our nation's responsibility to its own heritage which will be felt for decades to come."

Pullman, Washington   ROALD FRYXELL
1970   RICHARD DAUGHERTY

Palouse Canyon 10,000 years ago

Palouse Canyon

1

❖◖◗❖◖◗❖◖◗❖◖◗❖◖◗❖◖◗❖

THE SEARCH BEGINS

It was a day of discovery, although nobody knew it yet.

The setting was deep in Palouse Canyon, in the forgotten southeast corner of Washington State. A ranch bulldozer was clanking through powdery dust near an archaeological site, and a lone scientist walked behind the machine.

Roald Fryxell, the scientist, is a geologist. He is one of the leading authorities on the effects of the Ice Age in western America and a staff member of the Laboratory of Anthropology at Washington State University. Anthropology, the study of man, ties in closely with geology, the study of the earth, for a simple reason: man does not live in a vacuum. He lives in relation to surroundings. Therefore, if scientists are to understand early peoples, they must know about the land that the people traveled across and depended upon for livelihood, and about the climate. Geologists give part of the answer to these questions. They also help to date tools and skeletons and other evidence of man that is dug from within the earth, layer by layer.

13

Professor Fryxell was finishing work for his Ph.D. degree. For the last three summers he had camped in Palouse Canyon to work with Dr. Richard Daugherty, a recognized authority on the early men who inhabited North America during the close of the Ice Age and an archaeologist at the Laboratory of Anthropology. Archaeology, which is one branch of anthropology, is a study of history from the long years before man knew how to record events and thoughts. Instead of written accounts, archaeologists "read" the stories told by fire hearths that have been cold for tens of centuries, by broken spear points, by the bones of animals cracked open to get the marrow, and by skeletons of humans buried by long-ago families.

In the walls of Palouse Canyon nature has hollowed small caves

Small caves eroded beneath lava flows have sheltered Indians for thousands of years.

used by Indians until recent years. The material that man leaves behind him—skeletons, tools, garbage—lasts better in such caves than in the open. The caves give shelter from water and wind. The material simply lies there, buried and waiting. Daugherty and Fryxell had found a bonanza in one of the caves, or "rock shelters" as shallow caves often are called. For three summers the men had worked with other professors from Washington State University and a crew of students, digging and sifting the floor of the particular shelter. They named it Marmes Rock Shelter after the Roland Marmes family, owners of the sheep and cattle ranch on which it is located.

Dr. Daugherty had tested two other rock shelters, then concentrated on this one, which is close to where the Palouse River flows into the Snake River. Lower Monumental Dam was scheduled for

Dr. Richard Daugherty

A wild and empty land

construction on the Snake River, the tenth dam built by the Corps of Army Engineers to tame the Snake and Columbia rivers. The dams were changing the wild rivers into quiet passageways that ships will navigate inland from Portland, Oregon, to Lewiston, Idaho. Water, spinning the dams' generators, promises electricity. Unfortunately, however, the reservoirs behind the dams destroy forever the chance to study part of our heritage: they flood sites known to have been used by early man. Dr. Daugherty knew of seventy places used by Indians within the basin of the new Lower Monumental Reservoir alone. His mission was to rescue as much of the past as he could before it disappeared beneath the rising water.

Palouse Canyon is wild country. Most of the few ranchers who live there have no telephones, no mail delivery. Children ride

16

The Marmes Rock Shelter (left side of picture) is situated in canyon country that today is dry but that 10,000 years ago was moist enough for scattered evergreen trees.

seventy-five miles to school each day, bouncing by private car and bus over roads that are either dusty or muddy, depending on weather. The land seems hostile, hardly a place for man to have lived through thousands of years. Yet early man found there the basics he needed. The valley bottoms offered easy routes for travel. The river provided water, and plants and animals along it gave food. Heavy black cliffs of lava rim the canyon—and eroded into them are the rock shelters.

Dr. Daugherty felt that the Marmes Rock Shelter would be the best to dig. It is low enough on the canyon wall to have been easy for men to scramble up into, and the river is close enough for convenience in hauling water. The shelter faces east, so morning sun warms it even in winter. A bend in the canyon cuts off the worst of the wind. Surely men would have used this particular shelter for ceremonies or for burying their dead or for storing food. Perhaps some men might even have settled into it as a dwelling.

Digging proved Dr. Daugherty right. Rich finds included the skeletons of fifteen Indians dating from 200 to 8,000 years ago. The oldest were among the most ancient burials known in America—and far older than the Egyptian pyramids. The first pyramid is a mere 5,000 years old.

By studying the geology of the rock shelter's floor, Professor Fryxell could help determine the age of the ancient burials. White dust a foot thick lay above them, and there was no sign that it ever had been disturbed until the shovels of the archaeologists had dug into it. Therefore, bones lying beneath this layer already were in the rock shelter when the dust drifted in. The bones would be older than the dust, and luckily this particular dust could be identified and dated. It is volcanic ash from an eruption of Mount Mazama, a volcano in Oregon, hundreds of miles south of the rock shelter.

Microscopic characteristics helped Fryxell to recognize the ash.

18

Ancient burials lay within the floor of the rock shelter.

So did the position of the ash layer in relation to other layers in the floor of the shelter. About 6,700 years ago Mount Mazama erupted and gutted itself so completely that the peak collapsed, and Crater Lake now fills the hollow that was left. Ash rode the winds as far north as Canada. It fell day after day in a suffocating rain of white dust, building the telltale layer, which now lies beneath the accumulated dust of the thousands of years since the eruption.

Some of the burials lying under the ash blanket had been carefully made. A set of five matching stone knives lay with the bones of a young child, perhaps placed to help the child find the path to the spirit world. Other burials held spear points and shell beads, or charcoal where a small fire had flickered as token of man's eternal awe in the presence of death. The rock shelter must have seemed an attractive burial vault. It promised protection, and its floor was easy to dig into even with simple tools of wood and bone.

Some skeletons lay face down, buried only by the thickening dust of the years, with no evidence of ever having been tended. Nobody had positioned these bodies or buried grave goods beside them. Perhaps these men and women had crept into the shelter alone to die. Perhaps they had been killed by enemies, although this is not probable. Warfare was uncommon during the first thousands of years of Indian life in America. Early peoples lived in bands that were both too small and too poorly organized for war. They were widely scattered and busy with staying alive, season by season.

Animal bones also lay within the cave floor. Here was evidence of the meat supply that men chose from through the thousands of years. Carl Gustafson, a zoologist who also is on the staff of the Washington State University Laboratory of Anthropology, studied

Professor Carl Gustafson worked in the laboratory to identify animal bones. He found elk, deer, bighorn sheep, and antelope.

the animal clues. He identified elk, deer, bighorn sheep, and antelope, plus such small animals as rabbits and various rodents. There were also coyote and badger bones—carnivores, or animals that hunt flesh to eat. They preyed on other animals, as man himself had done. There were even skunk bones. Man coming into the shelter to escape a storm or to bury his dead sometimes must have angered the skunks—and the stench must have been the same then as now.

Puzzling over the burials and artifacts, the geological sequences and animal bones, Daugherty and Fryxell began to piece together the story of life at Marmes Rock Shelter. They worked it backward, beginning with the wire and buttons and shotgun cartridges found in the upper part of the shelter floor. These top inches belonged to the ranching era. It reached from the present back to one hundred or one hundred and fifty years ago, from material left by the Roland Marmes family to the early days of contact between Indians and settlers. Outside the shelter, near the river, the archaeologists found a bronze medal with the words, "Peace and Friendship," circling a pair of clasped hands. This was a Jefferson Peace

Jefferson Peace Medal was found outside the shelter.

Medal, one of a dozen specially made for Lewis and Clark to give to Indians whom they met on their trek across the wilderness continent in 1804-1805. Only four other medals of the original twelve ever have been found.

Beneath the evidence of white men were layers with a variety of stone and bone tools. Arrowheads beautifully flaked and notched from gleaming agate the color of caramel candy came from upper layers. Man had known where to get good stone by the time he made these, and he had taken the time to go there and get it or had set up trade routes. No agate is found naturally in Palouse Canyon.

Deeper within the floor, and therefore from longer ago, lay spear points. Some were fashioned of heavy basalt, the kind of lava that forms the roof of the shelter. It was easy to get, but too coarse a stone to shape into fine points, no matter how carefully a man worked. Other points were fine, made of harder, finer grained stone. At least some of these spears must have been hurled by atlatls, sticks used for leverage in throwing spears, and invented long before bows and arrows. The best evidence suggests that the bow and arrow dates from only about 3,500 years ago, but the atlatl belonged to Stone Age man. Interestingly, the earliest spear points show as expert workmanship as the most recent arrowheads. Man perfected the technique of flaking and grinding stone sometime in his dim beginnings as a maker of tools. He early gained full control of the technique and could fashion what he chose. Changes through the millennia, therefore, represent changes in the size of animals hunted or in the way points were hafted to shafts, but not changes in the technique of working stone.

No pottery was found in the Marmes Shelter. It is not known in the Northwest. Indians seem to have woven baskets as containers instead of shaping clay into pots. A few pieces of tattered mats still lay in the rubble of the floor, but nothing ancient. Plant fiber turns too quickly to dust.

Burials were removed intact from the rock shelter and taken to the laboratory for preservation.

Flat stone mortars together with pestles just the size to fit the human hand showed that women had learned to gather berries and wild seeds and to grind or pound them for food. Scrapers indicated that they knew how to tan hides, probably for clothing and for making into water bags.

One kind of shell kept appearing. They were small and gray, about the size and shape of olive seeds and, in fact, called olivella shells. They belong to a saltwater snail still found on Pacific Coast beaches, far distant from Palouse Canyon. They lay within the rock shelter in deposits as much as 7,000 years old.

These shells could only have come from salt water, and they therefore either must have been traded from the coast to Palouse Canyon or collected on long overland journeys. Furthermore, Dr. Daugherty noticed that most were drilled with tiny holes, suggesting that they had been strung as necklaces, for beauty or as money strings, wampum. This meant that by the time of the olivella shells, man at the Marmes Rock Shelter already had become more than a wandering hunter. He had contacts beyond his immediate homeland. New materials and new ideas were his.

Olivella shells had been drilled with tiny holes, evidently to be strung. Finding ocean shells two hundred miles inland indicated that early man had trade routes.

The story of the little rock shelter was fitted together slowly, piece by piece, and pushed ever farther into the past. But the new reservoir was to flood fifty miles of river bottom, and the stories of the other sites also needed to be salvaged. Daugherty moved on in 1965, and Fryxell continued to study the geology, both inside

Professor Roald Fryxell studied the geology of layers within the earth, "reading" the past of Palouse Canyon.

the shelter and in front of it toward the river. Roland Marmes offered to help by using his bulldozer to cut a trench that would open the layers of earth to view. This cross section would serve as a calendar of geologic time. From it, Professor Fryxell could puzzle out what happened to the earth through the hundreds of centuries since the Ice Age. The top of each layer might be an old surface where men and animals once walked and flowers bloomed. Or the old surfaces might have been riverbeds or lake bottoms or wind-blown sand too loose to support life. Roald Fryxell wanted to find out.

It was hot as he followed a few feet behind the bulldozer. Dust kicked up with each step and billowed in clouds as the blade bit still deeper. Dust powdered the men's faces, choked their noses, and gritted between their teeth. Sweat stuck their shirts to their backs. The dozer had cut twelve feet into the soft silt of the valley bottom, and the men worked now in a narrow bake-oven slot.

Suddenly, Fryxell saw a fleck of bone lying where the blade had scraped. He signaled Roland Marmes to stop, and bent to examine his find.

It was thumbnail size, gray with age. A second fragment lay close by. Fryxell sketched the positions of the two in his notebook and looked for more. He found a concentration of two dozen small pieces, some of them charred. He made notes of how they lay in relation to each other and to the layers of earth that showed in the walls of the trench. Then he picked them up and headed his truck for Washington State University, ninety miles distant in Pullman.

The evidence of man that already had been pieced together for Marmes Rock Shelter led to an expectation of still more. The site was ideal. The record must reach far, far into the past—if only it could be "read" in time.

Roald Fryxell knew what he was looking for as he walked behind the bulldozer that day of discovery.

2

⟐⟨⟐⟨⟐⟨⟐⟨⟐⟨⟐⟨⟐⟨⟐

MARMES I FLIES
TO WASHINGTON

Professor Fryxell could not know how valuable the new find was, but he could hope.

Arriving at the Washington State University campus, he wheeled his dusty truck through the gate and turned down the tree-shaded lane to the anthropology lab. He parked and gathered the drawings and the box with the fragments of bone packed in cotton. In his office he placed both drawings and box in the safe. For now, that was all. He was needed elsewhere.

Daugherty and Fryxell were directing a dig on the Pacific coast of Washington, as well as this one in Palouse Canyon. On the coast they were puzzling together the story of early Indians who hunted sea lions and even whales from canoes far at sea. So much archae-ological work needs to be done that scientists often have several digs going at once. This is especially true of salvage archaeology, where the construction of new dams and highways, or the pounding of ocean waves, threatens to destroy the evidence of the past.

It was November before Professor Fryxell could get back to Marmes Rock Shelter; five months had passed since he had found the new bits of bone. With him came both Daugherty and Henry Irwin, another Washington State University archaeologist. No dust flew as their wheels bumped along the ruts leading into the canyon this time, and as the men huddled in the trench, they shivered. Southeast Washington is desert-hot and dry through a long summer. But let the calendar say "winter," and the days bring rain, fog, snow, and the kind of cold that makes misery of fieldwork.

The three professors and friends who came to help them gently scraped the silt floor of the trench, using flat hand trowels and brushes. The bulldozer had shoved the bones Fryxell had found out of their original position. The fragments might even have been dragged down from the rock shelter; their story might belong up there instead of here on the floodplain in front of the shelter. What was needed was more bone—bone that was unquestionably undisturbed, that still lay in its original position.

A little beneath where the dozer had cut, the men found what they were looking for. Here were bone fragments that seemed in place, as they had been for centuries. A few had been crushed by the weight of the bulldozer passing inches above them. Some were charred, others not. There appeared to be several different types of bone. Such a group would not be likely to have occurred by chance; man probably had been present. The scientists looked for tools that would confirm their guess that this had been a human campsite.

Disappointingly, they found none. But the additional bone was potential treasure to take back to the lab. Their mood was one of tentative triumph as they drove out of the canyon and back to Pullman.

In the laboratory Professor Gustafson studied these new scraps. He identified some as elk bone; for the rest, he simply could not be sure. The texture of shattered bones often can be used for identification, or the shape of the ends of leg bones or toes will offer clues, or differences in the ridges to which muscles attach. Unbroken bones speak quickly and clearly to an expert—and Gustafson has spent years measuring and comparing the bones of various kinds of mammals, including man. But these bones were mere bits.

Work went slowly. Professor Fryxell returned to the trench as often as he could, but there were the results of the coast dig for him to analyze and write up, and he had classes to teach at the university. However, fleck by fleck, the handful of bone scraps grew larger, and finally a year and a half after the discovery of the first bone in the trench, Gustafson was ready to make an announcement. Much of the bone, unquestionably, was human. Several pieces clearly belonged to a skull.

Bit by bit the collection of bone fragments grew. Professor Gustafson said some were unquestionably human.

Another year passed. Downriver from the rock shelter, power cranes were lifting steel, and workmen were pouring concrete. Week by week Lower Monumental Dam rose higher. By Christmas its spillway gates were scheduled to shut, and the new reservoir would begin to fill. Two or three days after that, Daugherty and Fryxell guessed, water would be lapping the floor of Marmes Rock Shelter. Only the arch of the roof would stand clear.

Each Saturday and Sunday as winter faded into the early spring weeks of 1968, Fryxell drove several graduate students to the site, and together they puzzled out the geology. As each session ended, he mentally subtracted another week from the few months left until Flood Day. When it came, the water would end his study, whether or not he was finished and ready.

Fryxell wanted to complete his work on the geology and to settle the question of the bones. They lay twelve feet below the surface in a layer of earth that passed beneath the earliest layers of the rock shelter excavated so far. To a geologist this meant that

Lower Monumental Dam was rising higher. Water in its reservoir would reach to the site and end the dig; the archaeological team was racing a flood.

the bone fragments must be even older than the 8,000- or 9,000-year-old artifacts found in the rock shelter. This could only mean that they were as old as any human remains ever found in the Americas. Furthermore, the chance of documentation was ideal. Six years of intensive study by the Washington State University team had already gone into the site. Much of the archaeology, geology, and knowledge of past climate and plant and animal life already had been deciphered. Nowhere else in the Western Hemisphere had truly ancient human bones been found in such a documented setting.

In the rock shelter above the bones Fryxell now puzzled over, there was a layer choked with the shells of mussels from the river. The shells were at least 9,000 to 11,000 years old. The new discovery beneath this layer must therefore be at least as old as the shells and possibly older.

The shell deposit gave a minimum age for the bones, and another layer—below them—gave their maximum possible age. While cross-sectioning the layers of the earth, Fryxell had found silt deposited by a lake that had filled the canyon about 13,000 years ago. The human bones lay sandwiched between the layer with the mussel shells and ancient lake deposit. Consequently, they must be at least 9,000 to 11,000 years old; and they could not be more than 13,000 years old.

Man seems to have been in America more than twice this long. He evidently first arrived about 25,000 years ago—or possibly as long as 30,000 to 40,000 years ago. He simply walked across from Asia. The straight black hair, brown eyes, and brown skin of Indians even today are as Asian as American. So are a fold of skin at the inner corner of the eye, which both Indians and Asians have, and a faint blue-black spot on the lower back of both American Indian and Asian babies.

At the time the first Americans arrived from Asia, ice was blanketing the north and reaching southward as far as what today is the United States. This whitecap glistened across—and chilled—most of Alaska and Canada, on to Washington State, the upper Great Plains, and into Wisconsin, Illinois, and Ohio. The movement of this ice shaped the Great Lakes. It also shaped Puget Sound, in the Pacific Northwest.

Ice held a vast amount of the earth's water locked up—and this is still true. Today's glaciers, chiefly in Antarctica and Greenland, hold so much water that if they suddenly were to melt, the ocean would rise three hundred feet. Nations such as the Netherlands would disappear beneath rolling waves, and from New York to Tokyo barnacles would cover skyscrapers.

During four successive Ice Ages far more water was frozen into ice than is the case now, and this dropped the ocean level below what it is today. The first of these Ice Ages, somewhere between one and four million years ago, created a bridge of dry land between Asia and America. Then conditions changed, and water once more divided the continents.

By the time of the fourth Ice Age, man was living in Asia. He dug pits as shelter and roofed them with rib bones and hides from mammoths—huge, woolly elephants that then roamed in great herds, although not one remains alive now. These men were hunters. They had no agriculture. They simply followed the herds, moving camp as the grazing of the great beasts demanded and knowing well the need to cooperate among themselves. One man alone cannot track, kill, and skin a mammoth. He must cooperate or perish.

The land bridge from Asia to America, which had appeared again, was free of ice and an easy route, and so were long valleys threading western Alaska and Canada. Grass tinted the rolling country with green, and small willow, alder, and birch trees lined the banks of ponds and streams. Mammoths, two-humped camels, giant buffalo, and other Asian animals grazed their way to the new land. Human hunters and their families followed.

Land joined the continents for thousands of years during the Wisconsin Ice Age, the most recent of the four, although the width of the strip depended on the changing level of the ocean. At times the bridge of land would disappear, then again emerge.

About 19,000 years ago world climate warmed, and the glaciers started to melt. Water poured into the ocean and raised the level of the sea. The bridge slowly shrank, and by about 14,000 years ago it disappeared. Water lapped man's route from the Old World to the New and sealed his fate. He had become American.

In a surprisingly short time the descendants of these first Americans spread throughout their new territory, wandering, learning, and adapting. Each generation pioneered only a few additional miles, yet by 10,000 years ago—and possibly much earlier—man had traveled the entire distance from Alaska to the tip of South America.

Few signs of his passing remain. Archaeologists searched the Americas for half a century, but they rarely find evidence of truly early man. The population was tiny, the land enormous. Also, few types of evidence can last for thousands of years. Bone disintegrates and returns to soil, and pits dug for shelter fill and disappear.

About all that archaeologists can really hope to find are stones fashioned into grinders, choppers, knives, and other sorts of tools and weapons, or the charcoal left from long-cold campfires. Occasionally, there are tools made from bone. Tools tend to last better than unworked bone. The oils from a man's hand or processes of toolmaking such as heating seem to help preserve the bone. Once in a great while if soil and moisture conditions have been precisely right, there may be truly ancient human or animal skeletons. Newspapers then carry headlines: LAGUNA WOMAN'S SKULL BELIEVED 15,000 YEARS OLD; MINNESOTA MINNIE MAY BE 10,000 YEARS OLD; NEW FIND IN MEXICO DATES BACK 24,000 YEARS.

Most such claims for great age fail scientifically. There simply is not enough to prove them. Often the layering within the earth

33

has been so disturbed and jumbled that there is no way to tell the true order of the layers. Or a skull that tests as ancient in the laboratory will have been found years before, and scientists cannot now check how or where it originally lay. They cannot relate it to a whole story or be sure that it was free of chemical contamination that would throw off lab dating. Or occasionally a person who finds bones in an undisturbed position gathers them up and then later reports the discovery. Without meaning to, he has destroyed the only sure evidence of age; for unless an archaeologist can study the sequence of layers in relation to undisturbed bones lying in place, he cannot piece together a true story.

The finds from two digs in the Western Hemisphere may match the Marmes finds for age, although certain questions about each of them never can be answered. In 1953 an oil-well worker found a broken skull lying on the surface of a sand dune near Midland, Texas. He knew he might be looking at something valuable and was wise enough not to touch it. He phoned the anthropology department at the nearest university. Archaeologists pieced together the skull and dated it in the laboratory as at least 8,000 years old, and possibly 20,000 years. Unfortunately, search as they would, they could find no tools or animal bones lying close to the skull for a cross-check on age. Worse, the geology gave no clue as to how long the broken skull had lain there. In sand dunes, wind continually blows away old layers and deposits new ones. The story was out of sequence, with no way to reconstruct it.

The other lone skull that may be truly ancient was discovered near Mexico City, at Texpexpan, in 1949. Best guesses date this one as about 10,000 years old, but they forever will be partly guesses. The skull may have been from a recent grave that had been dug down into the ancient layers of the earth. Nobody studied the geology in detail before the skull was lifted out, so the question always will remain. There is no way to go back and check.

Fryxell knew the odds as he raced the flood at the Marmes site;

but hard work, luck, and expert knowledge finally were paying off. Still more human bone was being found. These new bits of evidence were also shattered, and each bone was fragile now that it was exposed to the air. Yet here at last were more than stray fragments. Here was an archaeologist's dream of an assortment.

Bennie Keel, another staff member of the Laboratory of Anthropology, and a group of select students from Washington State University and the nearby University of Idaho, were working with Fryxell by this time. It was the spring of 1968. Nearly three years had passed since the day of discovery behind the bulldozer. It had taken this long to prove that the bones were as old as they seemed, that they lay undisturbed. The delay came partly from the difficulty of studying and documenting each layer in the long sequence back to the layer with the bones, partly from the press of Fryxell's other work, and partly from lack of funds. Then with only nine months left before the site would be flooded, the earth at last began to yield its secrets.

Fryxell and Keel had dug a test pit at one side of the original trench. With the help of the students, who all had worked at previous important geologic and archaeological sites, they spent weekends shoveling and scraping. The team worked through a fifth consecutive weekend, and a sixth. Still nothing. They worked a seventh Saturday. Nothing. And then Sunday afternoon their trowels uncovered bone.

By now they were thirteen feet below the surface of the canyon bottom and four inches deeper than the blade of the bulldozer had been. This new bone could not possibly have been disturbed by the bulldozer. Carefully, Fryxell and Keel collected every scrap the trowels uncovered, and they also filled sacks with the sediment scraped from the floor of the pit. They were excited: they recognized one of the new pieces as a bit of human skull.

Back in the university laboratory, the two men washed the sediments through a fine sieve to save any tiny bits of bone that their

35

eyes might have missed in the field. For the next two days Keel cleaned and sorted pieces. The sieve repeatedly held useless gravel —and also fine pieces of bone from small animals and odd little hollow mineral "noodles." These had formed 10,000 years ago as carbonates in the soil had precipitated around the roots of living plants. Perhaps the "noodles" would serve as an added clue to past climate. Bennie Keel saved each one.

An expert from Poland, Dr. Tadeusz Bielicki, happened to be at Washington State University as a visiting lecturer when the new finds arrived. A specialist in physical anthropology, the comparative study of the human body, Bielicki had been examining the bits of human bone that Gustafson had separated from the fragments already brought in. He thought they might belong to a single skull and had begun to fit them together. Then came the new piece that Fryxell and Keel had found. It fit exactly into the middle of the other pieces, gleaned through three years of painstaking search. As that one gray scrap slipped into place and filled the hole, it proved that all the pieces were from the same layer. They had been *in situ*, undisturbed.

Slowly the pieces fit together into a human skullcap—Marmes I.

Carl Gustafson was working on the animal bones. He identified elk, deer, antelope, rabbit, and some kind of fish. All except the fish had been cracked open to get the marrow, and some had also been burned. Obviously, man had fed on these animals. Probably he had roasted the meat, then opened the bones for the marrow, which is extremely nutritious and highly valued as a food by primitive peoples even today. The cracked and burned bones established a relationship between the growing accumulation in Gustafson's office and the human bones down the hall in Fryxell's safe. The ancient floodplain by the Marmes Rock Shelter had been a "living site," a place where man had pursued daily activity. The Washington State University team could hope to reconstruct a fairly full story of the ancient past—if they could find the funds and if they could beat the flood.

Bennie Keel now discovered a third story. Cleaning a piece of bone the size of a broken pencil, he noticed two fine parallel lines definitely cut into the bone by man. That meant "worked bone," the term for any bone that has been fashioned into a weapon or tool, as opposed to bone that man has not shaped. As Keel continued cleaning and sorting, he found three more pieces that fit with this first one. They formed parts of a gently tapering cylinder perhaps originally ten inches long. Probably this had been the tip of a spear. Or it may have served as the shaft with an additional, harder tip attached.

Sharpened bone had tipped a spear. Two fine lines cut into the bone proved that it had been fashioned by man.

The evidence now was of several kinds: the partial human skull, the bones cracked open for marrow, and the weapon. Here was man himself, together with indication of how he had lived, what he had eaten, and how he had killed and prepared his food. Such a combination never before had been found in one place in North or South America in so clear a geologic context and as part of so long and continual a record.

Lights burned late in the lab night after night as experts worked over the various parts of the puzzle. The skullcap of Marmes Man was slowly fitting together, with Professor Grover Krantz of Washington State University taking over the work when Dr. Bielicki returned to Poland. The curve of the pieces helped him to fit them. So did the pattern of blood vessels, which once had lined the brain and still showed plainly on the inside of the skull. The sutures—the lines along which a skull fuses from baby form into rigid adult form—also gave clues of which piece went where.

When the job was done, Marmes Man told a surprising lot about himself. The sutures were not completely joined; therefore, Marmes Man had not been fully adult when he died. Probably he was in late teens or early twenties.

The shape of the head indicated a modern type of man, not a primitive "cave man." No one today would notice anything odd if Marmes Man could return, dress fashionably, and push a shopping cart along a supermarket aisle. He had full brain capacity and intelligence. Doubtless he did a better job of living by hunting than modern man would if suddenly thrown into Marmes' time and circumstances—and the ability to solve problems is one of the basic definitions of intelligence.

The skullcap gave one more hint of Marmes Man's life. The inside was fire-blackened, and most of the bone was thoroughly charred. Perhaps Marmes Man had fallen victim to cannibals. The elk had been eaten by men who broke open the bones; Marmes Man may have been on the same menu. His charred and broken

bones lay mixed with the elk bones. Early man, of course, sometimes cremated his dead, but the charred Marmes skeletal material
certainly had not been buried. Cannibalism was suspected.

One secret that the skull could not tell was sex. Marmes Man
may have been a woman. Nobody could be sure from the bone
fragments that had been found. A pelvis would give the answer
immediately, for a woman's pelvis is much wider than a man's.
But there was no help on this question in the top of a skull, a
piece of backbone, bits of broken ribs, a tooth, a wrist, and what
seemed to be arm or leg bone.

Either way, man or woman, the time had come to share the news
of the find with the public. Daugherty and Fryxell decided to make
the announcement in Senator Warren G. Magnuson's office in
Washington, D.C. Senator Magnuson had sponsored a bill permit-
ting federal agencies to help with salvage archaeology projects—
and certainly here was a salvage emergency in need of federal
assistance.

Marmes Man was to go to the capital with Daugherty and
Fryxell. They wrapped the skull in cotton and packed it into a
styrofoam box inside a small gray travel case. Now a delicate question arose. The case could not be sent as baggage. The Marmes
skull was too valuable to risk rough handling. Yet it did not seem
proper to shove the case under a seat, on the floor.

Fryxell had to go one day ahead of Dr. Daugherty. He took the
little case with the skull and hit on an answer to the problem while
boarding the plane. He talked the stewardess into giving him an
extra seat, and then he carefully strapped Marmes Man in by the
window.

Dr. Daugherty followed the next day, and the two college professors and the 10,000-year-old teen-ager completed their journey
to the special press conference called in the Senator's office. There
Marmes Man entered into the twentieth century while cameras
clicked and pencils scratched facts into reporters' notebooks.

A power shovel sped the work of opening the earth down to the ancient Marmes layers. Then hand shovels took over.

3

❖❖❖❖❖❖❖❖❖❖❖❖❖

DIGGING FOR CLUES

The race was on.

In Washington, D. C., Professors Daugherty and Fryxell had succeeded in gaining funds and the support of four important government agencies: the National Park Service, the National Science Foundation, the Army Corps of Engineers, and the Geological Survey. An emergency excavation of major proportions now could be launched. The National Park Service and the National Science Foundation had financed the first years of work at Marmes Rock Shelter; now the Corps of Engineers and the National Park Service cooperated to provide new funds. The Geological Survey offered a team of geology experts and laboratory analysts.

Newspapers reported the dig not only as an important one, but also as one of the most intensive manhunts ever launched by science. The story was carried abroad, and clippings began arriving back at Washington State University from papers in Europe and Southeast Asia.

At the site, a twenty-four-hour watch was posted with Washington State University and University of Idaho students volunteering their services. The opportunity to unravel the past was so awesomely great that no vandalism or unplanned interruption could be permitted. Other Marmes Men and their tools must be rescued before they drowned forever beneath the coming reservoir.

By the time Roald Fryxell and Richard Daugherty—and Marmes I—returned from the nation's capital, only eight months were left before the flood. In order for full-scale work to begin, more than twelve feet of dirt had to be removed from above the Marmes layer. The upper half of this had been dumped from the rock shelter during the earlier excavations when no one knew of the archaeological treasures that lay deep within the floodplain. The lower half was the undisturbed earth of the canyon bottom, built layer on layer through the thousands of years since Marmes Man had walked and hunted and dreamed there.

A power shovel could be trusted to remove most of the tons of silt and rock above the Marmes layer, and a crew with strong arms and backs could take care of the rest. But the digging itself is a small part of archaeology. The Marmes treasure would be flecks of charcoal and bits of broken bone. Equally important, the workers would have to study and record how one item related to another, and they would have to pinpoint the exact positions of each within the earth. Trained eyes, hands, and minds were needed—an expert crew as well as a strong one.

Time was short, but the excitement of this dig acted as a magnet. Graduate students in anthropology, geology, and nuclear physics signed up, most of them working on master's or doctoral degrees. It was as highly trained an archaeological crew as any that has been sent into the field anywhere in the world.

In archaeology, digging to find information destroys the source of the information. A hole is all that is left when the dig is over. The site is gone. There is no going back to take a second look or think further about a problem, except in the collections and

Work continued by hand once the sterile upper layers had been stripped away.

records. This is why an expert crew was needed. The records must be so accurate and complete that they can even answer questions nobody knew enough to ask during the digging itself.

A fairly standard archaeological system has been worked out, although for this dig several aspects of it were carried farther than usual. Each site is designated by an official number. The Marmes site bears the code number *45FR50*, assigned when Dick Daugherty first found the site in 1953, nine years before the first excavating began in the rock shelter. The *45* stands for the State of Washington, the forty-fifth state in an alphabetical listing before Hawaii and Alaska joined the Union. *FR* indicates Franklin County, where the site is located. And *50* means that Marmes was the fiftieth archaeological site found in the county.

A student held a surveyor's rod to help pinpoint the exact location of every bone and artifact.

A transit was used to read the rod.

Digging proceeded by pits measuring five feet on a side. Each was numbered according to its location, as determined with a surveyor's transit. Pit by pit and layer by layer, the students scraped the centuries from the floodplain and the rock shelter. Sometimes they used shovels and wheelbarrows, sometimes trowels and dustpans. Should a bone appear, they switched to soft brushes or even dentist's picks. The bone might be animal or human. It might be

When the richest layers were reached, students switched
from shovels to dustpans and trowels.

the first piece of an entire skeleton or a stray scrap from an ancient
garbage pile. Or it might be bone that had been made into a tool.

Each bit of bone was important—and each was likely to crumble.
For thousands of years it had lain undisturbed, preserved by a
favorable combination of geology and climate. To endure, it had
to have been buried while fresh in soil that was not very acid, for
acid soil soon destroys bone. There had to be minerals that soaked
into the bone, helping to preserve it, and there had to be protection from insect damage and frost through the long millennia. Yet
now exposed to air, a single careless touch might demolish an
ancient bone.

Sometimes the find was stone instead of bone. It was brushed out
with equal care, studied, and documented. Only then was it lifted
and sent to the field laboratory.

Every fleck of charcoal and sliver of bone were picked from the earth and saved.

The find might be indication of an ancient campfire or a hole dug by ancient man. Such holes continue recognizable even thousands of years after they have filled in because the original digging forever disturbs the natural layering of the earth, somewhat the way a hole poked into a layer cake and then filled with crumbs and frosting still continues to show.

A wedge made of elk bone is brushed free from the dust of the ages before it is lifted from place and sent to the field lab.

To keep track of each item in relation to the layering, students scraped the floors of the pits by "levels," each consisting of one complete, natural layer. A level might be the volcanic ash from the Mount Mazama eruption—a white layer and the easiest of all to recognize. Or it might be silt washed across the canyon bottom by ancient flood when the river had overflowed its banks. Twigs and leaves from broken plants would lie on the surface after such a flood had drained; new plants would grow and die. Rain would pound the surface, snow blanket it, sunshine scorch it. Insects and animals would live upon it and die upon it. The decay and the weathering would form a thin dark line, a record of that surface.

The digging proceeded from one such telltale line to the next, both on the floodplain and in the rock shelter. Frequently, the students would stop to sharpen trowels and shovels, then scrape on, peeling back the years. The dirt from each floodplain level was kept together in tagged wheelbarrows and delivered as a unit to a water screen, the next stage in the patient search.

Here other students washed the dirt through fine nylon mesh,

With the temperature above 100° F., the digging proceeded layer by layer, a slow peeling back of the pages of geologic and human history.

Shovels were sharpened often.

Sediments from the pits were washed through one-millimeter nylon mesh.

using water pumped from the Palouse River. Most of the sediment was fine and washed through, but larger bits caught in the mesh. The students watched these for charcoal, rodent teeth, fish bones, tiny snail shells, crayfish claws, ancient seeds—for anything other than gravel, and even for gravel if it looked unusual. Whatever they saw they picked out and sent to the field laboratory in a tagged glass jar, and with it went all the rest of the material that had caught in the screen. All would be checked under magnification in the lab.

The teeth and bits of bones and shells might give clues to the animals that lived here with Marmes Man. The remains of small animals actually may tell more about past conditions than those of

Tiny bits of bone and charcoal and shell, seeds and rodent teeth thousands of years old caught in the water screen.

large animals. Small creatures cannot range far. Whatever the climate is, they must endure it. Also, they are of little value to primitive man: he would not hunt a tiny snail or a mouse and carry it home to butcher and eat as he might an elk or even a rabbit. The bones and shells of small creatures found at the Marmes site, therefore, meant that those creatures had lived right there.

Knowing the animal life, a team of specialists could determine what plants must have clothed the land and served as food. From the plants they could tell a great deal about climate, for vegetation would have been as choosy about growing conditions then as now. Once this much was known, the team could figure a bit more about the life of Marmes Man. Did he need shelter from heat or from cold? Were building materials and firewood easy to find? Was food close by? During the summer of desperate digging, the entire emphasis had to be on finding, documenting, and salvaging evidence of all kinds. Analysis had to wait. When there finally was time for detailed study, a great deal of specific information came from the minute bits of evidence. For example, Gustafson identified pine marten and red fox bone. Both of these are creatures of the evergreen forest, and therefore the bones gave a good indication of how different vegetation and climate were in Marmes' time compared to the semidesert grassland of today.

Work also went by levels in the rock shelter. More tools and bones were found within the shelter than down on the floodplain because the shelter had attracted and concentrated man's use and also had protected whatever he left behind.

A dry screen was used at the shelter to shake and sift dirt from each level of each pit, much as the water screen was used on the floodplain. Worked bone often showed up in the dry screen, or there might be a piece of sharpened bone or a stone with an edge flaked for use as a crude scraper. Any bucketful of dirt might add something new.

51

Shells were common in the screen. Most were freshwater mussels, which must have been gathered by long-ago families and carried to the shelter for dinner. This same kind of shell had been chemically dated by radiocarbon to establish the age of the layer above the Marmes bones as between 9,000 and 11,000 years old, providing the minimum age for Marmes Man. The abundance of the mussels and of two other kinds of mollusks clearly demonstrated the presence of a large year-round water supply in the past, and one of the mollusks indicated there would have been rainbow trout in Marmes time. This type *(Margaritifera)* lives as a parasite on trout during its larval stage. Finding the shells of the adults therefore meant that the proper host must have been present for the larvae —and that meant trout.

As the earth was opened, Professor Fryxell and one or two advanced students spent a great deal of time squatting on their heels, staring at the pit walls. With a trowel, Fryxell would scrape the wall; then the men would look and look until they could see fine differences between the various cross-sectioned layers. When they saw them well enough, Fryxell would trace the lines. Occasionally, he would find a geologic fault, a place where the earth had shifted

Professor Fryxell used his trowel to trace the geologic layers that showed in the wall of an excavation pit. Rodent burrows, 10,000 years old, had filled with sediment and produced oval deposits.

Once the geologic layers had been traced, graduate students made precise scale drawings.

and raised a section of the layers out of line with the rest—or dropped them—disrupting the evenness of the layering. Or there might be ovals of one soil within a layer of a different sort. These were the filled-in burrows of ancient muskrats and ground squirrels.

Whatever Fryxell saw, he outlined with the tip of his trowel. Two of his graduate students then drew the pit walls to scale, using one inch to represent every two feet. They drew each layer, each fault and rodent hole, each boulder, and even each stone down to one-half inch in diameter.

A fence diagram was made from the scale drawings.

Such drawings are usual at archaeological digs, but one of the students carried them two additional steps at the Marmes dig. Working with Fryxell, she gathered the drawings from the past six years of work and used them to mock up a three-dimensional paper model of the rock shelter excavations. This was needed for the emergency project, in order to correlate the new trenches and discoveries with the earlier work. Called "fence diagrams," these paper models occasionally are used to help mining engineers visualize bodies of ore or oil in relation to the surrounding layers of earth, but the technique rarely is applied to archaeology. The diagram looked like a misshapen egg carton, with each hole representing a five-foot square of the excavation. The layers were drawn on the sides of the "carton's" holes.

From the fence diagram, the next step was to make a full model of the shelter with the excavations inked onto plexiglass. This would show precisely how the layering had been before the dig and could be used over and over to check relationships between one deposit and another—extremely valuable because the original layering was slowly becoming rubble as the dig progressed. The model gave a chance to "go back" and look again at what really no longer was there.

Still another kind of record was made: "monoliths" and "peels."

Next, the diagram was converted to a scale model of the rock shelter.

These are actual samples of pit walls and floors, which were preserved and taken to the Laboratory of Anthropology for study and storage—a "library" of layered sediments, the only one of its kind in the world.

For the monoliths, the crew soaked resin into a section of a wall that showed particularly clear layering or that had special significance. When the resin hardened, they could place a board against the face of the section and slowly, carefully, cut and tie a long column of the wall to the board. The section then could be lifted out to become a three-dimensional, permanent record.

The peels were taken in a similar way. The surface of a pit wall or floor was soaked with liquid latex rubber, and thin cloth was then pinned against it. More latex was applied to bond the cloth to the soil. When dry, a veneer of undisturbed soil could be peeled free and taken to the laboratory.

As the digging progressed, Fryxell kept watch for new geologic evidence. From the previous study in the rock shelter, he already had worked out a sequence of events in Palouse Canyon. There had been a great flood 19,000 years ago, well before Marmes Man. This was while glaciers of the last Ice Age still gripped the northern world, reaching across Canada to the upper edge of the plains states. A lobe of this ice had dammed an enormous lake near what today is Flathead Lake, Montana.

The ice dam broke and released a torrent of water, estimated at three hundred to five hundred cubic miles in volume. This raging flood cut Palouse Canyon, and other canyons, into the ancient lava flows of the Columbia Plateau. Boulders and debris swept nearly to the mouth of the Columbia River, and Portland, Oregon, stands now on deposits laid down then by the flood.

Another major geologic event Fryxell traced was the lake that had filled Palouse Canyon about 13,000 years ago. He could read its signs in delicately bedded layers of silt, which could have

A "peel" preserved one of the ancient surfaces from Marmes time. Polygons indicate frost action 10,000 years ago.

been deposited only in deep, quiet water. Plainly, this part of the floodplain, beneath the Marmes material, had been a lake bed. As work progressed, a thin seam of white volcanic ash was found in the lake deposits. One of the Geological Survey's visiting experts, Dr. Ray Wilcox, meticulously examined the tiny grains of ash with a microscope and a newly developed device called an electron microprobe.

Dr. Wilcox concluded that the ash was identical to that from an eruption of Glacier Peak, in the Cascade Mountain Range far northwest of Palouse Canyon. This eruption is known to have taken place about 13,000 years ago, and consequently its ash could be used as a key to the age of the lake. The flood and the lake that followed it furnished the maximum possible age for Marmes Man. He had to have come sometime after these two geologic events, perhaps exploring the canyon floor soon after the lake had drained.

The floor of the rock shelter gave evidence of the climate in the past, which Fryxell fitted in with other types of evidence. Until sometime after 14,000 years ago, Ice Age glaciers had reached within about one hundred miles of Palouse Canyon. The climate was damp and cold, and the floor of the rock shelter faithfully recorded this: great amounts of rock had fallen from the ceiling during that period and lay now in the deep layers where the crew was digging. Frost had formed in cracks and pried the rocks loose. Later the climate had warmed; there was less frost and less rockfall, and this showed in the upper layers of the shelter's floor. Fryxell could correlate the amount of rockfall the students had to dig through with what the climate had been in the past centuries.

As excavation progressed in the earliest layers, dark cracks shaped into a pattern of polygons were uncovered. At first they seemed to resemble the ordinary cracks that form as mud dries, but checking further, Fryxell realized that they more likely had been caused by severe frost, such as occurs today in Arctic regions. The degree of rockfall from this same period confirmed the cold climate, and so did a new discovery by Professor Gustafson. He identified a fragment of skull as Arctic fox, an animal that lives only in cold environments.

The Mazama ash represents another geologic event that Fryxell carefully traced at the Marmes site. Mere inches of ash seemed to have fallen 6,700 years ago, but it blew into drifts a foot and a half thick inside the rock shelter, and on the floodplain it had been thick enough to clog the channel of the drought-stricken Palouse River. For the next eight or ten centuries, no men used the rock shelter, except for an occasional lonely burial. Life in much of the Northwest already had been made difficult by severe climatic change from the earlier cold and moist period to a time of warmth and drought. The destructive ashfall must have even further complicated it—although the exact effect would depend on the time of year that it fell. There would have been little harm to plants during the winter months, but if the ash fell in spring as tender new shoots were coming up, it may have smothered growth. Where it lay as a thin blanket, it probably benefited vegetation through the next few seasons by acting as a mulch, helping to hold the scant moisture within the soil. But where the ash drifted thick, it must have taken years for the meager rain and pioneering vegetation to settle the powdery white dust and begin to enrich it into soil. Within the shelter, rock fell from the ceiling and helped to form a new floor, covering the loose ash—and man returned.

Standing in the trenches at the dig, Professor Fryxell's height spanned 5,000 years of geologic history, from the layers at his head to those at his feet. By puzzling out how each had developed, he was able to help date the archaeological finds as the dig progressed. Once he had completed the geologic documentation, the thick upper layers could be removed with a bulldozer, and work could progress into the lower, older layers. However, as a final precaution Fryxell wanted other geologists to check his conclusions. He asked the United States Geological Survey to send one of its top experts in the science of stratigraphy, the field of geology that deals with the order of layers within the earth. In response, Dr. Harold Malde flew from Denver to the Marmes site to confer with Fryxell and other geologists and soil scientists. The men studied the walls of the trenches and confirmed the geologic record. The stratigraphic drawings were completed. The bulldozing began.

To cross-check the geological evidence of age, Fryxell and Daugherty also gathered samples of ancient charcoal and bone for radiocarbon dating. Any organic material, plant or animal, may be dated by this method in a specially equipped nuclear physics laboratory. The principle is simple. Cosmic rays raining down on the atmosphere from outer space continually change a tiny fraction of the nitrogen there into radioactive carbon, which is called carbon 14, or simply ^{14}C.

Plants take up this ^{14}C from the atmosphere by photosynthesis at a steady rate, and animals get it from the plants they eat. All living organisms, therefore, have radioactive carbon in their tissues. At death they stop absorbing it, and what they already have starts to decay radioactively.

The decay occurs at a fixed rate that is the same for all types of organic matter, through all time, everywhere in the world. In 5,730 years, half of the ^{14}C disappears. In another 5,730 years, half of what remains disappears; after another 5,730 years, half of that is gone. In the laboratory, physicists can measure the amount of ^{14}C still in charcoal or bone or plant fiber. They then subtract this from the amount that is normal for all living tissue and convert the answer into the approximate years since the organism was alive. Measurements are made in terms of the rate of disintegration as the radioactive carbon gives off electrons.

For example, say that bone from a newly dead animal is to be

60

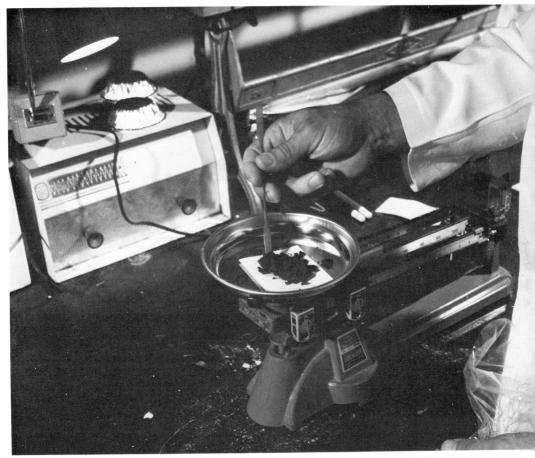

Samples of charcoal from the site were dated by the radiocarbon method.

checked. It will send out twelve rays of a certain type each minute. But if the physicist checking it gets a reading of only six, he will know that the bone is not fresh but rather is from an animal that has been dead for 5,730 years. If he finds only three rays per minute, he will estimate that the animal has been dead about 11,460 years. And so on.

The method is fairly accurate back to about 30,000 or 40,000 years (about six "half-lives). At least it is accurate in principle. In practice, radiocarbon dating is far from simple. Scientists have worked with the method only since the late 1940's which is not long enough to have perfected it. For example, recent findings show that the rate of carbon 14 production in the atmosphere may have varied by as much as 10 per cent at certain times, instead of holding steady as formerly was believed. This could throw off some dating by a much greater error than previously was thought likely.

Also, it now is known that not all organisms absorb radioactive carbon at exactly the same rate. Certain plants and animals—or

Radiocarbon-dating laboratory

parts of them—do not concentrate enough to provide a reliable sample after death. Or, even if the concentration during life and disintegration after death has held steady, a third factor may enter: contamination.

The root of a living plant may push into an ancient firepit and add fresh carbon 14 to charcoal that has been losing its stored supply for thousands of years. Or the opposite may happen. Water may seep through the firepit and leach out part of the stored carbon 14. Taken to the lab, charcoal from the first example will date younger than it actually is; it has too much ^{14}C because of the new root. In the second example, the diminished ^{14}C will give too old a date; more radioactive carbon is gone than would have happened without the leaching.

Even with problems, however, dating by radioactive carbon helps greatly to understand the past. It provides one more tool in a scientist's kit. Fryxell and Daugherty picked samples where contamination seemed the least likely, and they took them from varying spots within the same level. They sent them to different laboratories to be analyzed. If dates from the different samples, run by different labs, cluster around the same age and if they check with geological evidence, they can be trusted. In the early years of work at the Marmes Rock Shelter, radiocarbon dates had been run in the atomic physics laboratory of Washington State University. Now, during the emergency salvage, Dr. Meyer Rubin of the United States Geological Survey and head of one of the world's outstanding radiocarbon-dating laboratories repeatedly traveled from Washington, D.C., to the site to collect samples for ^{14}C analysis. All of the samples were checked in his lab, and some were rechecked in the radiocarbon lab at Yale University—a cautious double testing that is part of scientific procedure.

The results of all the measurements were consistent. Without question, Daugherty and Fryxell were deciphering human and geologic events that stretched back 10,000 years.

Residue from the water screen was carried to the
field lab in plastic bags and buckets.

In the lab students checked the residue, searching through magnify-
ing glasses for minute fragments of evidence.

4

◆〴◇〴◇〴◇〴◇〴◇〴◇〴◇〴◇

IN THE LAB

A tent and trailer served as a field lab.

Whatever caught in the water screen went there to be checked—the gravel, the rodent teeth, snail shells, and bits of bone. The scale drawings and the notebooks in which each student wrote up his work also came to the lab. Here was documentation of what the soil had been like, exactly where deposits of charcoal or bone had lain, and how artifacts had been positioned. Notes are not for the writer's use: they are one of the permanent records of the dig. They have to be neat enough and clear enough that anybody can understand them any time, even years after the dig is finished.

Artifacts, human bones, and animal bones first were drawn and photographed as they lay within the earth, and described in the field notes; then they were carried to the lab. Receiving them, lab students cleaned each artifact or bone and inked the Marmes site number plus the pit and level number directly onto it. In this way each item was permanently indexed in relation to the scale drawings, the plexiglass and paper models of the shelter, and the field notes.

Professor Gustafson would be studying the animal bones after the dig. He could check a number and know exactly where that piece came from. This would tell him whether the animal could have been hunted by Marmes Man or had belonged to a different level and therefore had lived at a different time.

Or say that Bennie Keel and Henry Irwin were studying the spear points and knives. Did certain styles belong to the same period? Or had workmanship remained unchanged through centuries so that weapons and tools that looked alike actually belonged to different periods? The numbers would help answer. If they showed the same level, the artifacts must be of the same age. If they showed separate levels, the ages must also be separated.

Spear points began to accumulate in the lab. Coming from

Each artifact was marked in India ink with the code number of the Marmes site and the exact location where the artifact had been found.

Marmes time, they were large and heavy, for early men hunted by patient stealth and stalking. They wounded animals with spears or lances and waited for them to die by bleeding, rather than killing them outright. The bushmen of Africa still hunt this way; poisons they use are not strong enough to kill large animals.

Some of the points were made of bone, such as the one found with the first Marmes skull. Others were of stone that had been chipped. In addition to the points, there were scrapers, choppers, grinders, hammerstones, knives, and drills made of stone of various kinds—jaspar, basalt, opal, obsidian.

Stone tools are surprisingly quick to make. The anthropology lab has a special "rock knocking" corner where students and professors practice flaking obsidian into points and blades as a way of deepening their understanding of what life would have been in ancient times. Obsidian is glassy black and hard; it flakes easily. A perfect point can be shaped in twenty minutes, once a person has learned the basic technique. A simple scraper takes only three or four minutes. Early man may have worked even faster—and this might explain why his points are easy to find today: lose one, and it was quicker to make a new one than to search for the old one.

Stone tools often had remarkably sharp edges. Dr. Irwin and Dr. Daugherty once skinned a freshly butchered cow, using two obsidian tools, to find out how efficient stone would have been for early man. One of their tools was a perfect knife blade, which they fashioned specially for the job; the other was an unworked flake of obsidian with its edge left as it naturally split from the core stone. Surprisingly, they found the flake too sharp for convenience. It kept cutting through the hide. The obsidian knife was much easier to control.

It may be that early man chipped edges onto some tools to dull them rather than to sharpen them. Both of the stone tools—the flake and the knife—stayed sharp better than a modern steel hunting knife that Dr. Daugherty also tested on the cow.

By midsummer the crew was bringing new finds to the field lab almost daily, and this was fortunate. Time was short. In early September money for the dig would be gone, and by December the reservoir would rise. One day the discovery was the jaw of a coyote or wolf. Another day it was a giant elk, 10 per cent larger than any alive today. These bones were the vertebrae and hindquarters of the elk, with several ribs close by. Where was the rest? Had this much of the animal been carried here to roast? Or were the bones the spare-parts supply of a toolmaker?

A mystifying bird claw was brushed free in one pit. Professor Gustafson painstakingly compared it with the claws of modern birds and identified it as owl. Time scarcely had affected it. The toes curled back as though belonging to a fresh-killed bird, instead of one that had lain within the earth for 10,000 years. Two chips of stone lay above and below. Evidently, they had been bound to the claw, perhaps with plant fiber, which had disintegrated. A hole

Dr. Henry Irwin made a careful scale drawing of the elk bones after they had been brushed free without disturbing their position.

The owl claw lay for 10,000 years sandwiched between two flakes of stone.

pierced the leg bone. Possibly the man who owned this claw had worn it about his neck to help fight off evil. Or perhaps it belonged in the medicine bundle of a priest, brought out for a curing ceremony when someone was ill, or it may have helped men find prey and strike silently and surely in the manner of an owl, one of the great hunters of nature.

More points, scrapers, and choppers appeared. Some lay at the same depth as the original Marmes bones, which were in a deposit of silt about four inches thick. Others came from eighteen inches deeper in the floodplain. Fryxell thought this lower layer must have formed mere decades earlier than the Marmes layer. Perhaps the tools at this lower level had been made, used, and lost by the men whose bones were found in the higher layer. The Palouse River overflowed its banks often during that wet closing of the Ice Age, and the floodplain grew layer by layer. Rain and snow pelted down, and the waters of the swollen river often raged across the entire canyon bottom. The water swirled silt as it came, then dropped the load when the flood had spent its force. A thick layer could build in a short time during that period, where later— with the climate in a hot and dry period—it might take centuries for the same thickness to be deposited.

Dr. Irwin often sat in the back room of the lab trailer to work over the growing collection of artifacts. He made drawings of each point and compared them with his knowledge of what had been found at other sites and with published descriptions and drawings. Clearly, these Marmes points were extremely old, among the oldest known in the Western Hemisphere. The slender bone point found with the Marmes skull and some of the stone points looked very much like those from sites where early man had killed mammoths.

These mammoth-site points are the famous Clovis points first found near Clovis, New Mexico, but now discovered also in Alaska, Canada, each of the forty-eight adjoining states, and south as far as Mexico—the oldest and most widespread points in America. Clovis points are of stone, thin and lance-shaped, measuring as much as four to six inches long and an inch and a half wide. Notches cut into their bases probably to help fasten the points to wooden shafts. Clovis points always lie among the bones of mammoths, marking sites where early man had hunted. Occasionally, other kinds of animal bones also may be present, but always there are mammoths. The bones and points lie in layers that average 11,000 to 12,000 years old.

Slowly the collection of points grew, spanning from 10,000 years ago (at the right side) to the recent centuries of life at the Marmes site.

Folsom points are nearly as old as Clovis points. They are found more commonly, but not over so wide a territory. The bones of extinct giant buffalo always are found with the Folsom points, and there may also be other animals. These points are long and narrow and notched at the base, although in a different style than the Clovis points. They further differ from Clovis in having a groove running nearly the length of the point, from base to tip. This fluting may have helped to attach the blade to the shaft, or perhaps it thinned and lightened the point so that the lance could be hurled farther. Maybe it caused blood to flow faster when the weapon had found its mark. Maybe it simply was a matter of style, a decorative touch.

By patient study Dr. Irwin would be able to make a detailed comparison between the Marmes points and those from other sites. Certainly the style of the Marmes stone and bone implements suggested great age, which tied in with the geologic evidence.

Now came astonishing news: students had found pieces from another human skull—Marmes II.

The new fragments lay about twenty feet from where the first Marmes skull had lain and were at the same depth. No skulls ever had been found at the ancient sites where Clovis or Folsom points were uncovered. Man had left his evidence—the slain mammoths and buffaloes, and his tools—but not his own bones. Yet the Marmes site was yielding not just one human and his tools, but two! And the dig was not done. There might be even more.

Grover Krantz, the physical anthropologist of the team, headed back to the lab at the Washington State University campus with the pieces of the new skull and a scattering of other human bone found nearby. He faced a jigsaw puzzle. Of course each piece had its place, but try and find it.

Here was a heavy splinter. Did it come from a leg or an arm or a rib?

71

Here was a flat piece the size of a nickel. Part of a shoulder blade? A skull?

Unquestionably, this piece was from a skull. It curved, and a suture line still showed. But was it from the same skull as that other piece or a separate one?

Professor Krantz worked for a week, then was ready with a few answers. The new find was more than one person. Two bones that should fit together didn't. They overlapped, repeating the same portion of the skull. There could be only one explanation: the two pieces were from two persons.

Ten skull pieces and several teeth did belong together. Evidently, Marmes II was a young child. Part of a jaw had been found with a first molar still in place. This is a heavy chewing tooth that

Professor Grover Krantz fitted a piece of the Marmes II skull against a comparative skull.

children get at about age six. The tooth showed very little flattening, which indicated that the Marmes child used it only two or three months, then died.

Another tooth still was deeply embedded in the jaw. This was the second incisor, which children cut at about age eight. From the two teeth Krantz could say that the skull belonged to a child at

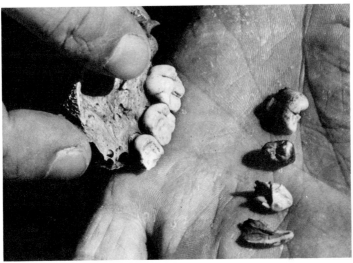

Teeth from the Marmes II child were compared with teeth in a modern jaw.

least six years old and not yet eight. Children of all races, through all of time, get teeth within a few months of the same age. A jaw with teeth, therefore, gives an ideal measure of age for a nonadult skull.

Newspapers throughout the nation added the discovery of Marmes II to their earlier accounts of Marmes I. Television cameramen drove the dusty road to Palouse Canyon to record the finding of the "oldest man in America." Archaeologists and geologists from museums and universities and professional societies came to see for themselves. Any who could arrange the time stayed to help dig. Dr. Marie Wormington, President of the Society for American Archaeology and a world-famous expert on ancient man, came to visit and left so excited by what she had seen that she withdrew the professional paper she had submitted for the International Anthropological Congress meeting in Tokyo, and instead she spoke to the assembled scientists about the Marmes discovery. She described it as the most significant discovery in American archaeology in the last quarter century, since the original finds of Clovis and Folsom points.

Public interest mounted as new finds were announced. In spite of bad roads and dust and heat, visitors started making their way through the rough country to marvel. As many as a thousand thronged the site on weekends, and students added the conducting of tours to their work of digging. Here was our American heritage. People wanted to see for themselves before it disappeared beneath the flood.

And then still another new find was announced—this time a bone needle about the size of a modern steel embroidery needle. It was broken in three pieces, but all had been found, and they fitted together perfectly.

Marmes Man sewed with a bone needle as fine as a modern steel embroidery needle.

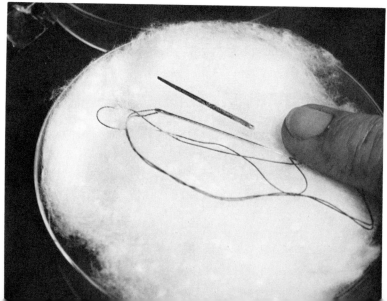

The eye piece had been discovered in the water screen as dirt from the pits was being washed. The lab crew had spotted the other two pieces while sorting through the material caught in the screen. Here were three tiny slivers of bone, only an inch and a quarter long when fitted together. Yet they all had been found and recognized.

No bone needle from the Western Hemisphere matched this one for age and fineness. Similar needles are known in Europe from sites about 20,000 years old, but in the New World all the needles found have been large and coarse. American peoples other than Marmes Man must have used equally fine needles, but the odds weigh against an archaeologist finding them. It was the water screen—an unusually painstaking technique—that had saved the Marmes needle. Even then, it would have been lost if the first piece had not caught crosswise. If it had entered the screen on end, it would have washed through and been lost.

Lying on cotton in the lab, the needle seemed a fragile splinter from the past. Yet for its owner it had meant survival. Marmes Man had campfires, but no real house to hold the heat. He may well have depended on tightly stitched fur clothing as shield from the Arctic cold of his Ice Age world. Perhaps he also used the needle to sew waterproof bags of elk and deer hide, using sinew as thread. He then could carry water and could cook in the bags by adding stones heated in the fire.

The idea for a needle meant a breakthrough for primitive man. Manufacturing a needle is not hard. Dr. Irwin had made one from bone during a dig in Wyoming. He shaped it in about half an hour, then spent another ten minutes drilling a hole with a stone perforator.

Sewing is also easy. The first hand to hold a needle made the same simple pushing and pulling motions that a woman's fingers make today. Stitching is easy—but so is using a wheel.

It is the idea behind a tool that comes hard.

75

A broken knife blade lay with the cremation hearth.

5

MARMES III

Through the scorching summer weeks, the crew scraped and shoveled, stopping often to heave out rocks fallen thousands of years ago from the ceiling of the little cave. No shade shielded them from the full blast of sun and temperatures that climbed above 120° F. on ten consecutive days. They were excavating an *old* floor of the cave, well out in front of the present roof overhang, for the cave has gradually shifted location through the years. It continually erodes deeper into the cliff, and it slowly shifts higher as rocks fall from the ceiling and raise the floor level.

The pit now cut sixteen feet below where the cave floor had been when the excavating began. At this depth a new find was made. Bits of bone began appearing—lots of them. All were small pieces, and all were charred. Examining them, Dr. Daugherty felt that this must be a hearth where ancient man had returned his dead to the earth by cremating. The hearth lay about four feet below the layer of ash from Mount Mazama and therefore had to date from before the eruption. But how long before?

Rock rubble fallen from the ceiling of the shelter lay between the volcanic ash and the hearth, and Fryxell estimated that it would have taken at least one or two thousand years for the deposit to build four feet deep. This would mean that the ritual flames must have burned here 8,000 or 9,000 years ago, or maybe more. The Marmes cremation site would be the oldest known anywhere in the world. A basalt knife blade was the only tool found at the level of the hearth. Evidently, during this period no one had lived in the shelter or worked in it or used it for storage. It belonged wholly to the dead.

Students began the job of sorting the charred bones. They separated finger bones, toes, pieces of long bone (such as leg or arm),

The bits of charred human bone were sorted to separate them by type—fingers and toes, pieces of skull, arm bone, leg bone.

skull, vertebrae. Professor Krantz would check them all in the laboratory. If certain joints were present, he could tell sex and age—even from small pieces. By measuring the thickness of skull fragments, he could sort out which pieces belonged to the same individual, which to different individuals. Eventually, he announced the remains of at least five persons—two adults and three children between the ages of eight and fourteen.

Deep blackening of the bone on both sides suggested that only skeletons had been committed to the fire, not whole bodies. The newly dead must have been laid somewhere else and the bones later gathered and carried back to the shelter for ritual cremation. Perhaps cremation explained the charring of Marmes I, not cannibalism.

Or maybe it was cannibalism after all.

There were hundreds of pieces to study, but slowly Professor Krantz fitted bits together and assembled partial skulls. A curious

Professor Grover Krantz compared the skullcaps he had pieced together from the Marmes fragments with skulls from modern Indians.

difference in the pieces was becoming apparent as he worked: within a single skull some fragments were deeply blackened, yet immediately adjoining pieces were only lightly blackened. Perhaps these people had fallen victim to cannibalism, and in the process of cleaning up after the feast, bits of the shattered skulls had been thrown casually back into the fire and so become doubly charred. Krantz thought the sequence had been burning, breaking, then burning again.

One arm bone showed knife marks, such as are found on the bones of animals that have been butchered. However, the same sort of cutting could have been in connection with cremation.

Men as early as Marmes time apparently seldom buried their dead. Archaeologists never have found burials of extreme antiquity, and without the type of care and protection associated with burial customs, it is not surprising that so little ancient human bone is discovered. Both Marmes I and Marmes II skulls lay on what had been the surface of the canyon bottom at the time the skulls found final rest. Nobody had opened the earth and placed the bodies within; there had been no ceremonial burial. In fact, where were the rest of the skeletons? Little but the broken heads had been found. The skulls perhaps had been separated in connection with cremating—or with cannibalism. Sure answers may never be known.

The end of August drew near. So many finds of value had been made that the Marmes crew began to hope a way might be found to protect the site from the coming reservoir. Then they could have more time to dig. Fryxell and Daugherty guessed that about 75 per cent of the site lay beyond reach in the time remaining to them.

By the close of the month two shreds of hope appeared. At Senator Magnuson's request the Corps of Engineers was studying the possibility of a levee to wall off the archaeological site from the

Into the night the Corps of Engineers drilled, planning a levee to protect the Marmes site from the new reservoir.

flood, and they provided more money so that the dig could continue through the fall. Lower Monumental Reservoir still would have to fill on schedule or the winter storms would gravely undercut a railroad bed and other installations that had been made along the reservoir banks; but the Marmes site might be saved. Crews drilled late into the night, probing the depths of the canyon bottom, checking where and how best to build the protective levee.

Now came more news—spectacular news. A third skull was found on the floodplain!

Marmes III lay below the cave within fifty feet of Marmes I and II and at the same depth. This new skull, too, was shattered and

81

Dr. Henry Irwin brushed Marmes III with glue to strengthen the ancient bone.

partial. It lay like a broken coconut shell. Dr. Irwin softly cleaned the dust of the millennia from the pieces, then brushed on a weak solution of water-soluble glue to strengthen the bone.

Grover Krantz came to the pit to fit the pieces together. They belonged to a person eighteen to twenty-five years old at death, he said. Sex could not be determined. There was no charring.

Fryxell and Daugherty decided to lift out Marmes III in place, within the block of earth that had cradled it through the long years. In this way the record of the earth would be preserved unquestionably, forever. It would be there in the laboratory, physically present for anyone to study, as well as represented in the scale drawings and field notebooks. Other finds from the rock shelter had been taken to the Washington State University lab in this way. On an earlier dig a cast holding a burial had been too big to carry in the lab door and up the stairs, and the engineering department had loaned a power crane to hoist it through a window.

Dr. Irwin brushed more glue onto the skull, letting it soak in. Then he packed loose clean sand around the skull to support it and turned a wooden box upside down over it for protection. Students took turns cutting free the sides and bottom of the block that held the skull. It was to be a large block—three feet long by eighteen inches wide and deep—so as to preserve a generous sample of the layers holding Marmes III.

Marmes III was to be lifted out in a block.

A jagged boulder the size of a kitchen stove caused problems. It had fallen perhaps 11,000 years ago from the cliff above the rock shelter, and the skull of Marmes III had come to rest by it. Only the protective bulk of the boulder had prevented the shifting channel of the Palouse River from washing the skull away. Even so, the great stone was in the way now. Days of work with hammer and chisel went into cutting it to free the block of earth holding the skull.

Finally, all was ready. The block was free. It had been soaked with a solution of resin, then wrapped in canvas and soaked with plastic to make a hard cast. Two-by-four boards formed a frame. One of the students drove the backhoe into position above the pit. Others fastened chains around the cast. The motor revved. The chains tightened. And Marmes III lifted clear.

Never could heavy machinery be used more gently, nor could more hands—and hearts—reach to help steady the transfer of an item. From the long resting place of the ages, Marmes III swung to the bed of Fryxell's waiting truck. The chains were removed, the motor started—and as the wheels of the truck started to turn, a gust of sudden wind lifted the dust of the pit and swirled it into the faces of the scientists. Marmes III began the final journey.

Work continued, still a race against the reservoir, with the question of the levee unsettled.

A tiny graver was found in one pit, a stone drill point that could have been the one to pierce the eye into the needle.

Four more needles and a bone awl appeared in the water screen and the field lab. All were broken.

Bone, including the jaw of a bighorn sheep, was scraped free at a level several inches below where any had previously been found. The position of the pieces suggested hunting. A single flake of stone lay close by. There were flecks of charcoal.

Each new pit seemed to produce a new find; but still there was

Gently the team lifted Marmes III from his resting place of the centuries.

no final word on the levee. Fall rains began. The crew wore slickers and troweled on. Would it all be over in a few weeks, or would the site be saved?

At last a phone call came from Washington, D.C., to Pullman. Senator Magnuson had arranged for a proposal to be placed before Congress to authorize construction of a levee to save Marmes Rock Shelter. The Senate had voted yes.

Roald Fryxell flew from the university campus to the site to pass the word. Everyone cheered what promised to be sure victory, and Fryxell returned to the anthropology lab.

Within hours bad news followed the good. The measure had been killed in the Senate-House conference committee, and Congress was adjourning.

It was afternoon when this second call came, and a hard rain poured from the heavens. Yet Fryxell climbed back in the airplane. The mess tent at the site was leaking badly, but there the crew sat resting and happy with the good news of the morning. Now Fryxell told them the latest word. Hearts sank and muscles and minds grew suddenly weary.

Fryxell flew out just before dark, hardly able to see through the rain and gathering gloom. Only by following the headlights of cars inching along the highway below could the pilot find the field at Pullman and land.

However, Senator Magnuson was not yet through. As a last resort he was appealing directly to the President, asking his personal intervention. Letters began flooding the White House asking that the site be saved. They came from private citizens, educators, and scientists throughout the nation. Americans previously had given generously to salvage temples and carvings in Egypt when the building of the Aswan Dam on the Nile River threatened them. But there had never before been widespread public support for salvage archaeology within our own country.

Tension mounted, and finally in October word came. It was good. The Corps of Engineers was instructed to build a levee. Within days of the announcement, legislators, archaeologists, geologists, crewmen, spectators, newsmen, and cameramen stood in the mud with umbrellas hoisted and dedicated the levee. Senator Magnuson himself turned the first spade of earth, joined by the Assistant Secretary of the Interior, Clifford Pautzke, President Glenn Terrell of Washington State University, and representatives

Senator Magnuson stood with Fryxell and Daugherty to dedicate the beginning of work on the protective levee.

Pieced together, the Marmes III skullcap and a tooth found with it were displayed at the dedication.

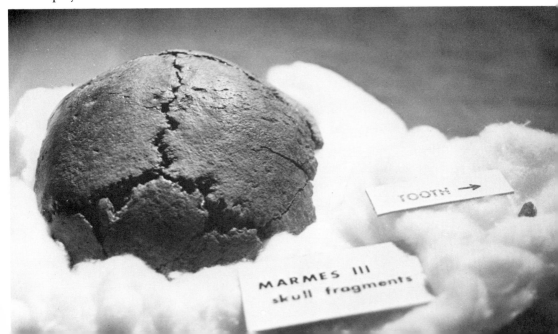

TOOTH →

MARMES III
skull fragments

of every major archaeological and geological organization in North America, plus representatives from the Smithsonian Institution, the National Park Service, the National Science Foundation, the Geological Survey, and the Corps of Engineers.

Climax and anticlimax built fast.

The skies continued to pour torrents onto southeast Washington. The floodgates of Lower Monumental Dam could not be counted on to carry such a volume; they would have to be closed. This would start the reservoir filling, and water would quickly reach to the pits. Two or three days would do it.

The end of February loomed as the new date for closing the spillway of the dam and raising the pool, an extension of two months beyond the earlier December deadline. The Corps of Engineers pushed hard to finish the levee in time. It would curve around the floodplain site and press against the cliff at each side of the rock shelter. A trench forty feet deep was dug and filled with bentonite clay, which would swell when wet. On top of this the engineers would mound an earth-fill fifty feet high, faced with crushed stone. It would rise ten feet above the highest water of the reservoir.

Protection seemed assured. The crew began to talk of another ten years of digging to fully explore the story of Marmes Man and the world he knew. Fryxell estimated that an area of about three hundred by four hundred feet at the Marmes depth should be as rich as the portion already investigated. The Marmes layer evidently was part of an early floodplain of the Palouse River, which happened to have remained intact—one of very few such remnants. About three-quarters of this ancient surface had not yet even been sampled, but with time enough the story could be fully uncovered and pieced together. A museum would be built. The pits themselves would be stabilized to show the actual excavation, and perfect replicas of the Marmes skulls and tools would be placed in position exactly as the originals had lain.

But none of the dreams came true.

First, it was the weather. The hardest winter on record in the Pacific Northwest set in. Palouse Canyon, usually a pocket of mild winter weather, was blanketed with a foot of snow. Supply tents were crushed, and temperatures dropped to an unprecedented 30° F. below zero as if to increase the misery of continuing work. Heavy equipment ground to a standstill, and the archaeology crew —now reduced to minimum numbers—was trapped in trailers without electricity or running water. Canned goods burst from the cold.

Then a sudden thaw arrived, accompanied by a disastrous warm wind. Melting snow flooded the river, and cakes of ice clogged it. Waters came to within less than a foot of overtopping the unfinished levee. Archaeologists and engineers spent a frantic night of emergency work in a driving rain, and as morning's light finally took over from the darkness, they could see that they had won this particular battle. The water was subsiding.

Slowly and painfully, the Washington State University crew struggled to make up for the precious time lost in the storm. They rigged lights and worked nights as well as days. They removed geologic specimens and continued deep testing for signs of man. They excavated by placing heaters against solidly frozen sediments to thaw them.

But time ran out. Trouble even more dire than the winter weather arrived. The levee itself was not holding.

A porous layer of gravel lay deep beneath the archaeological site, and it was acting as a conduit. Inexplicably, the Corps of Engineers had failed to seal it off, although they knew it was there. When the dam was partially closed, water poured through this gravel and came under the levee. It rose almost as fast within the "protected" area as outside of it. Pumps could not begin to keep pace with the flow, and it was clear to Fryxell and Daugherty that the situation was hopeless.

The only goal left was the forlorn one of preparing the site as well as possible to withstand the flooding, in case further excavation should be possible sometime in the future. Two squares next to where Marmes III had been were especially valuable. Cultural material seemed almost sure within them, and the crew did all they could to save them by building wooden cribs and caps of heavy timber around and over the unexcavated squares.

Next they lined the entire site with plastic sheeting and called for dump trucks to begin bringing sand to fill the excavations. For four days and nights the trucks churned through mud to the site, working around the clock much of the time in order to beat the

The excavations that had yielded Marmes Man were lined with plastic to ready them for abandonment.

Dump trucks worked around the clock to backfill the trenches that had been so carefully dug.

deadline. They dumped their loads at the rim of the trenches, and students and professors handpacked the sand around fragile portions of sediment such as pit walls and corners, burying the unfinished work of seven years. Just before dawn on the fifth day, the last load was brought. The trenches were filled. The sand was capped with a veneer of gravel at the expected pool edge to prevent waves from attacking the sand fill and sediment beneath. The bones and campfires and tools of Marmes Men still lying in unsampled parts of the site would not wash away or be shifted out of true position.

And maybe someday . . . if the water could be drained off . . . or when the Palouse portion of the reservoir silts in, as it will do in from fifteen to twenty-five years . . .

"You can't just shrug and walk away," Professor Fryxell said. "Not from a site like this one."

More than 4,000 square feet of old surfaces had been investigated in the rock shelter and floodplain. Ten thousand cubic yards of dirt had been removed mechanically, and about seven hundred had been excavated by hand with shovels, trowels, dustpans, brushes, and dental picks. One hundred and thirty-three special features had been recorded; 243 scale drawings made; 2,170 documentary photographs made. More than 15,000 square feet of the layering within the earth had been recorded. Two hundred and fifty artifacts had been found, and 2,400 catalog entries had been made to record and describe them adequately.

Seven years of unusually productive research had cost $250,000. The useless levee cost $1,500,000.

Damage to the site, now beneath the lapping water, will come mainly from the enormous weight of the water compacting the layers of earth and perhaps warping or distorting some of the beds. But the trench walls should be all right. The supports the crew built should prevent major slumping and mixing of the beds.

The reservoir flooded the site, lapping nearly to the roof of the little cave.

The stone artifacts will not be hurt by the wetness or the compaction. Bone may be damaged. Some tools and human skeletons and animals bones may be badly affected, depending on their exact condition before the submersion and during any future drying. Bone still within the old floor of the rock shelter will be damaged especially easily because it had lain dry through the long years and now is soaked. Only the arched roof of the little cave stands above the reservoir today.

Perhaps work can be resumed in a decade or two or three if the site is drained and carefully let dry to regain its structural strength. Our cultural heritage still lies within the earth. In the last around-the-clock days before final defeat, the crew had found new concentrations of material in layers deeper than the Marmes layer and also out to the side of where previous finds had been made.

For now, however, nothing more can be done.

Marmes Man ranks as the oldest man in America to be fully documented. And with fantastic luck, Marmes *Man* is not one, but at least nine! There are the Marmes I, II, and III skulls, part of a fourth from the floodplain, and the charred bones of an identifiable five persons from the cremation hearth. Nor is this all. There are also fifteen human remains taken from the rock shelter during the first three years of work.

The total presents a far longer sequence of human skeletal material than has been found at a single site ever before, anywhere, in the Western Hemisphere. More than 10,000 years of life in and around the little rock shelter are proven by man's bones. Furthermore, man's tools also span the years, and the bones of animals he preyed upon. In addition, there is detailed knowledge of the changing environment he has known, from Ice Age conditions to desert and the broken prairie of today.

Nowhere in North or South America has there been a comparable dig—so far. There will be others of course. Someday a new "oldest man" will be found, for part of being human is an unquenchable urge to know, to find out, to understand. A discovery such as Marmes Man fills a gap or two and eases the way toward further discovery; but the quest knows no end. Man always has pondered his past. Crouched close to the flicker of night fires, he wondered and listened as priests told of mythical beginnings. Today, men bending over laboratory desks to piece together bones or to compare stone points still wonder.

The Corps of Engineers built the levee in time, but it failed. Water rose within its "protecting" curve as rapidly as without.

INDEX

95